Ludwig (Ludvik)
MOSER
King Of Glass

PRICE GUIDE

1988

1988
PRICE GUIDE

for

Ludwig (Ludvik)
MOSER
King of Glass

by
Mural K. Charon

(cover) Ludwig Moser, 1833-1916,
is shown here in 1915 at the age of 82
holding his granddaughter.

INTRODUCTION

When we first published <u>Ludvik (Ludwig) Moser, King of Glass</u>, we were aware that many people would like prices to be attached to the glass but, because most of the glass is in limited quantities or one of a kind, we decided not to attempt to prepare a price guide with the book. Since the time the book was issued, the demand for the price guide has not diminished but has increased. We have decided that we will do our very best to give you an indication of value. We would still recommend that in any case you check more than one source before selling your glass.

To get the best indications of value available, we have checked with dealers nationwide and in most cases we have given a range of prices or, if they were close, we averaged them.

There are still several one of a kind pieces that we consider pure works of art which can only find a value at the formal auction. In these cases we must decline to guess what the collector might pay.

We have keyed the price guide to the book so that the page number is given with the price list and explanation of the item. This way you can carry the price guide with you to auctions, antique shows and malls.

1987 Price Guide
$2.50

With Ludvik (Ludwig) Moser, King Of Glass - FREE

Copyright© 1987 by Mural Charon
ISBN No. 0-917231-09-0
Published by
Charon/Ferguson Divison of
Ferguson Communications Publishers
Hillsdale, Michigan

PRICE GUIDE

VASES

Page 47-   Plates 85, 86 - Clear crystal, shaded to light green, band of gold leaf also on base, tall stem with fused jewels. $300 to $400.

Not pictured - applied birds in the wine cups. $550.

JUICE GLASSES

Page 49-   Plate 88, 89 - Clear crystal shaded to amethyst, gold leaf rim white enameled scrolls, red jewels, applied and filigree in gold. Signature on the base. $250.

Page 50-   Plate 90, 91 - Lavish all over decoration on this emerald green glass, gold leaf bands top and bottom, fern and vine gold decor, glass beads. $250.

Page 51-   Plate 92, 93 - Pale amberina glass shaded to smokey color, corolene glass beading, large grape leaves, grape clusters, leaves and vines. $260.

Page 52-   Plate 94, 95 - Rich cranberry glass, heavily gold leafed, leaving a sort of "window", freize work in the gold leaf, small shield in window, matching champagne. $295.

Page 53-   Plate 96 - Emerald green glass, gold band with an intricate design, violet florals with trailing vines, leaves and buds surround the glass below the band. $350.

Page 54-   Plate 97, 98 - Classical Lily of the Valley decor on gold leaf band from the rim to the base at an angle, remainder decorated in fernery and florals in gold leaf. $150 to $200.

Page 55   Plates 99, 99A - A commemorative glass with a metal holder, Green glass decorated with petite glorals, grape clusters and leaves in gold. The holder is in twisted grape stems and leaves. $495.

UNUSUAL DRINKING VESSELS

Page 65-   Plates 120, 121 - Unusual horn of plenty hunting vessel, applied base overall 9½" high. Horn is rich cranberry with gold leaf flowers and tendrils, clear glass base has gold leaf florals. $700.

Page 66-   Plate 124 - Two hunters drinking vessels are curved like horns with applied handles, 124 is light green glass with a hunter with his gun and dog. Gold leaf acorns and oak leaves. $750.

Plate 123 - This similar drinking vessel is a cobalt blue color which is cut to clear in places. The applied handle has white enamel design which is also on the main body. $550.

Page 67-   129, 130, 131, 132, 133 - Cylindrical toasting cup in cranberry, clear applied handle with gold leaves on it. Three gold bands and large leaves with corolene beads and branches, chain enameled. $395 to $550.

Page 69-   Plates 135, 137, 140 - A three handled presentation or award cup in cranberry glass with clear handles. Small flowers are green, pink and blue shades. White beading and shield white enameled. $395 to $550.

Page 71-   Plates 141, 143 - A drinking vessel like a Pilsener glass with a handle, completely gold leafed with a band variation 1/3 of the way down. Small florals and leaves enameled in red, orange, white, blue and green tops the gold all the way down including the base. $395 to $550.

Page 72-   Plates 144, 144A - A 10" sea green Romer cup with elaborate grape and grape leaf decoration. Blue, red and green enamels are lightly covered with gold leaf. Beatles and gold leaf punts add to the decoration. $1,800.

Page 73-   Plates 145, 145B, 145C, 145D - A clear vase decorated with the famed home of Adolph Hitler, the "Berghof" and the Bavarian Alps painted on both sides. It is signed "Moser" and is such a significant historical piece and one of a kind, that no value can be placed on it.

Page 76-   Plates 147, 149 - These show brilliant paintings on a glass plate signed by "Moser" and numbered. Exquisite art work and probably one of the kind. No accurate value can be placed on such work.

Page 77-   Plates 150A, 151A - Pale green opaque decanter similar to celedon. Applied glass grapes enameled leaves and vines.

$1,750.

Page 78-   Plates 154, 155, 156, 157 - Cranberry glass decanter set with 8 liquors, housed in a cranberry egg. Beautifully ornamented with gold leaf, enameled leaves and stems, latch is a womans head in brass and it sets on brass feet. One of a kind, priceless.

Page 80-   Plates 159, 160, 161, 162 - A jewelry box which is highly enameled with birds, florals, leaves and stems on unusual brown glass.

$900 to $1,200.

Page 82-   Plates 163, 164 - Clear glass decanter, beautifully decorated with a man and woman, each on a horse and in an embrace.

$900.

Page 83-   Plates 166, 167 - A boula bowl, painted with a fantasy of mythical characters in song and dance. Has polished brass cover and base.

$2,200.

Page 84-   Plate 168, 169 - Stick vase with ferns, vines, butterflies, berries and beatles, beautifully ornamented all over with enamels. $700.

Page 85-   Plates 170, 171 - Saddle glass ornamented with leaves, knight, vines and flowers, enameled on blue glass. $450.

Page 86-   Plate 172 - Triangular footed bowl decorated with enameled leaves. $650.

Plate 173 - Two handled vase in celedon like glass. Enameled and jewels fused to it, gold leaf handles, other decorations. $900 to $1,000.

Page 87-   Plates 173A, 174 - Matching 173, this single handled pouring pitcher, also has a dragon which is in gold leaf and beautiful enamels. $900 to $1,000.

Page 88-   Plates 175, 176 - Round hinged glass container of deep cranberry, enameled Lily of the Valley decoration on both the base and lid. Ribbed base. $550.

Page 89-   Plates 177, 178 - Almost round vase decorated with enameled vines and leaves and a large, colorful bird on a branch, it has four ribbed snail feet. $3,200 to $4,500.

Page 90-   Plates 179, 180 - Highly ornamented in gold leaf, this decanter set of cranberry glass has a personal coat of arms on it. Because it is one of a kind, a specific price is difficult to determine.

Page 91-   Plate 181 - A large covered Romer cranberry glass drinking vessel highly decorated with gold leaf and enamels including a knight in armor. $2,200.

Plate 182, 183 - An emerald green decanter set with gold leaf decorations of acorns and oak leaves. $2,500.

Page 92-   Plate 184 - This is a clear glass, tall handled drinking vessel, ornamented with leaves and flowers and a magnificant tropical bird, with enameled gold leaf. $3,200 to $4,200.

Page 93-   Plates 185, 186 - A unique decanter shaped like a falcon hunting bird with the falcons head on the stopper, heavily gold leafed and enameled. Sits on feet and tail. $900 to $1,000.

Page 94-   Plates 187, 188 - A cup and saucer in opaline glass, decorated with gold leaf and an enameled cherub in bright colors. $475.

Page 95-   Plates 189, 191 - Vase decorated in the rare cameo technique with the Moser signature in the design. $1,600 to $2,200.

Page 96-   Plates 207, 208, 209, 210, 211, 212, 213 - This beautiful five piece dresser set in cranberry glass, delicately decorated with large and small acorns and vines in gold leaf. A priceless set and cannot be priced. Has original label.

Page 100-   Plate 194 - A vase with fish and birds enameled on blue glass which is wavy near the top. $3,200 to $4,500.

Plate 195 - A drinking glass like a horn which curves to make a handle and sets on a pedestal. Decorated with gold leaf and enameled flowers. $625.

Page 101-   Plate 196 - This plate shows ten pieces of Moser glass that appear separately elsewhere in this book.

Plate 197 - Three matching pieces including a heavy incised vase, a wine glass and a juice glass. Clear to sea green glass decorated with gold

Vase $550.
Wine $295.
Juice $250.

Page 102-   Plates 198, 199 - Decanter and three handled liquor cups in deep green glass. Decanter handle and spout somewhat exaggerated. Wicker like decoration around the body of the decanter. Gold leaf also on cups and top of decanter. $750.

Page 103-   Plate 200 - A blue glass candle holder on a stand with a gold leaved handle. More gold leaf decorations around the candle holder. $650.

Plate 201 - A handled drinking vessel in beautiful blue glass heavily ornamented with gold leafing, flowers, and leaves. $275.

Page 104-   Plate 202 - An unusual 3 handled drinking vessel in smokey glass, decorated in enamels with one of Moser's fantasies. $475.

Plate 203 - A vase or flower bowl which is almost round and is heavily enameled with miniature florals and gold leaf. $650.

Page 105-   Plate 204 - A goblet in clear glass with a tall stem and a single color used on the glass in intalgio. $295.

Plate 205 - A vase or flower bowl in clear to green glass, that is etched and on a low pedestal. $475.

Page 106-   Plates 214, 215 - Highly ornamented glass plates with gold leaf and enameled florals, leaves. $525.

Page 107-   Plate 216 - Five pitchers that are all heavily gold leafed and ornamented in various styles and sizes. $225 each.

Plate 190 - Another view of the vase shown in 189 and 191, page 95.

Page 108-   Plate 136, 139 - A three handled drinking vessel of cranberry glass with clear glass handles. Ornamented with gold leaf and enameling. $395 to $550.

Page 109-   Plate 56A - Another view of the green to clear glass vase in plate 197, page 101.

Plate 119 - Another closeup of beetles of plate 116.

Page 110-   Plate 134 - Another closeup of plate 129.
               Plate 148 - Another closeup of plate 147.

OTHERS NOT SHOWN IN THE BOOK

TABLE WARES: CUPS AND SAUCERS:

1.   Rich coloration of green, cranberry with gold leafing. $250.

2.   Clear to cranberry and other rich coloration all over leaf decor. $275.

3.   Fused glass acorns or grapes, leaves trailing vines. $375.

4.   Miniatures of cup and saucers, in decorated motifs of cherubs on opaline glass. $275.

5.   Any of his unusual shaping, applied claw handles, decorated or gold leafed. $250 to $350.

PERFUMES OR ATOMIZERS

1.   Cut to clear, intaglio cutting. $250.

2.   Highly decorated in various decors in color. $300 to $450.

3.   Miniature lay-down perfume with chain attached. $250 to $350.